SPIDER-MAN
MYSTERIO RISING

SCHOLASTIC SPIDER-MAN: MYSTERIO RISING. Contains material originally published in magazine form as AMAZING FANTASY #15, MARVEL AGE SPIDER-MAN #12, MARVEL ADVENTURES SPIDER-MAN (2010) #17, SPIDER-MAN: MASTER PLAN #1 and ENTER THE SPIDER-VERSE #1. First printing 2019. ISBN 978-1-302-92101-9. Published by MARVEL WORLDWIDE, INC., a subsidiary of MARVEL ENTERTAINMENT, LLC. OFFICE OF PUBLICATION: 135 West 50th Street, New York, NY 10020. © 2019 MARVEL No similarity between any of the names, characters, persons, and/or institutions in this magazine with those of any living or dead person or institution is intended, and any such similarity which may exist is purely coincidental. **Printed in Canada.** DAN BUCKLEY, President, Marvel Entertainment; JOHN NEE, Publisher; JOE QUESADA, Chief Creative Officer; TOM BREVOORT, SVP of Publishing; DAVID BOGART, Associate Publisher & SVP of Talent Affairs; DAVID GABRIEL, SVP of Sales & Marketing, Publishing; JEFF YOUNGQUIST, VP of Production & Special Projects; DAN CARR, Executive Director of Publishing Technology; ALEX MORALES, Director of Publishing Operations; DAN EDINGTON, Managing Editor; SUSAN CRESPI, Production Manager; STAN LEE, Chairman Emeritus. For information regarding advertising in Marvel Comics or on Marvel.com, please contact Vit DeBellis, Custom Solutions & Integrated Advertising Manager, at vdebellis@marvel.com. For Marvel subscription inquiries, please call 888-511-5480. **Manufactured between 5/17/2019 and 6/18/2019 by SOLISCO PRINTERS, SCOTT, QC, CANADA.**

10987654321

SPIDER-MAN
MYSTERIO RISING

SPIDER-MAN CREATED BY **STAN LEE & STEVE DITKO**

COLLECTION EDITOR **JENNIFER GRÜNWALD** ▪ ASSISTANT EDITOR **CAITLIN O'CONNELL**
ASSOCIATE MANAGING EDITOR **KATERI WOODY** ▪ EDITOR, SPECIAL PROJECTS **MARK D. BEAZLEY**
VP PRODUCTION & SPECIAL PROJECTS **JEFF YOUNGQUIST** ▪ BOOK DESIGNER **JAY BOWEN**

SVP PRINT, SALES & MARKETING **DAVID GABRIEL** ▪ DIRECTOR, LICENSED PUBLISHING **SVEN LARSEN**
EDITOR IN CHIEF **C.B. CEBULSKI** ▪ CHIEF CREATIVE OFFICER **JOE QUESADA**
PRESIDENT **DAN BUCKLEY** ▪ EXECUTIVE PRODUCER **ALAN FINE**

PETER PARKER WAS AN ORDINARY TEENAGER, UNTIL HE WAS BITTEN BY A RADIOACTIVE SPIDER AND GAINED AMAZING POWERS!

SPIDER-MAN!

LIKE COSTUME HEROES? CONFIDENTIALLY, WE IN THE COMIC MAG BUSINESS REFER TO THEM AS "LONG UNDERWEAR CHARACTERS"! AND, AS YOU KNOW, THEY'RE A DIME A DOZEN! BUT, WE THINK YOU MAY FIND OUR *SPIDERMAN* JUST A BIT... DIFFERENT!

SAY, GANG, WE NEED ONE MORE GUY FOR THE DANCE! HOW ABOUT *PETER PARKER* OVER THERE?

ARE YOU *KIDDIN'?* THAT BOOKWORM WOULDN'T KNOW A CHA-CHA FROM A WALTZ!

PETER PARKER? HE'S MIDTOWN HIGH'S ONLY PROFESSIONAL WALLFLOWER!

Stan Lee & S. Ditko

V-789   1

As you may have gathered, Peter Parker was far from being the biggest man on campus! But, his uncle Ben thought he was a pretty special lad...

You're not foolin' **ME**, Petey! I know you're awake -- and it's time for school!

Gosh, Uncle Ben--you're worse than a room full of alarm clocks!

As for Pete's aunt May, she thought the sun rose and set upon her nephew!

I cooked your favorite breakfast, Petey--wheatcakes!

Don't fatten him up **TOO** much, dear! I can hardly out-wrestle him **NOW**!

The faculty at Midtown High were also fond of the clean-cut, hard-working honor student!

Keep up the good work, Parker, and you're sure to rate a scholarship when you graduate!

I'll do my best, sir!

But alas, other teen-agers can sometimes, unwittingly, be so very cruel. To a shy young man...

Sally, I, eh, was wondering if you're busy tonight...?

Peter, for the **UMPT**eenth time, you're just not my type...

...not when dream boats like Flash Thompson are around!

I admire your good taste, doll! Get lost, bookworm!

Look, there's a great new exhibit at the Science Hall tonight! Would any of you like to go with me?

Science Hall! Hah! **YOU** stick to science, son! **WE'LL** take the chicks!

Yes, for some, being a teen-ager has many heart-breaking moments!

See you around, bookworm!

Give our regards to the atom-smashers, Peter!

Some day I'll show them! =SOB= Some day they'll be sorry! --Sorry that they laughed at me!

SCIENCE EXHIBIT

EXPERIMENTS IN RADIO-ACTIVITY

OPEN TO THE PUBLIC

ROOM 30

2

AND, A FEW MINUTES LATER, PETER PARKER FORGETS THE TAUNTS OF HIS CLASSMATES AS HE IS TRANSPORTED TO ANOTHER WORLD -- THE FASCINATING WORLD OF ATOMIC SCIENCE!

AND NOW FOR A DEMONSTRATION OF HOW WE CAN CONTROL RADIOACTIVE RAYS HERE IN THE LABORATORY...

BUT, AS THE EXPERIMENT BEGINS, NO ONE NOTICES A TINY SPIDER, DESCENDING FROM THE CEILING ON AN ALMOST INVISIBLE STRAND OF WEB...

A SPIDER WHOM FATE HAS GIVEN A STARRING, IF BRIEF, ROLE TO PLAY IN THE DRAMA WE CALL LIFE!

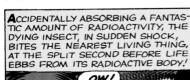

ACCIDENTALLY ABSORBING A FANTASTIC AMOUNT OF RADIOACTIVITY, THE DYING INSECT, IN SUDDEN SHOCK, BITES THE NEAREST LIVING THING, AT THE SPLIT SECOND BEFORE LIFE EBBS FROM ITS RADIOACTIVE BODY!

OW!

A-A SPIDER! IT BIT ME! BUT, WHY IS IT BURNING SO? WHY IS IT GLOWING THAT WAY??

MY HEAD-- IT FEELS STRANGE! I-I NEED SOME AIR!

LOOKS AS THOUGH OUR EXPERIMENT UNNERVED YOUNG PARKER!

TOO BAD! HE MUST HAVE A WEAK STOMACH!

WHAT'S HAPPENING TO ME? I FEEL-- DIFFERENT! AS THOUGH MY ENTIRE BODY IS CHARGED WITH SOME SORT OF FANTASTIC ENERGY!

HONK! HONK!

WRAPPED IN HIS THOUGHTS, PETER DOESN'T HEAR THE AUTO WHICH NARROWLY MISSES HIM, UNTIL THE LAST INSTANT! AND THEN, UNNOTICED BY THE RIDERS, HE UNTHINKINGLY LEAPS TO SAFETY -- BUT WHAT A LEAP IT IS!

THAT WAS ONE EGGHEAD WHO WON'T DAYDREAM ANY MORE WHEN HE CROSSES A STREET!

YOU CAN SAY THAT AGAIN!

3

WHAT'S COME **OVER** ME! I–I'M SCALING THIS WALL JUST AS EASILY AS I CAN **WALK!**

MOMMY! LOOK AT THE MAN WALKING UP THE SIDE OF A BUILDING!

THAT'S THE LAST HORROR MOVIE I TAKE **YOU** TO, YOUNG MAN!

IT'S **INCREDIBLE!** I REACHED THE ROOF IN JUST A FEW SECONDS!

WHAT'S **THIS??** I CRUSHED THIS STEEL PIPE AS THOUGH IT WERE **PAPER!**

IT'S THE **SPIDER!** IT **HAS** TO BE! SOMEHOW -- IN SOME MIRACULOUS WAY, HIS BITE HAS TRANSFERRED HIS OWN POWER -- TO **ME!**

I CAN WALK DOWN THIS CABLE AS EFFORTLESSLY AS THE SPIDER ITSELF CAN GLIDE ALONG ITS WEB!

I–I'VE GOT TO HAVE TIME TO THINK! I'VE GOT TO PLAN WHAT TO **DO** WITH THIS UNBELIEVABLE ABILITY WHICH FATE HAS GIVEN ME!

A FEW MINUTES LATER...

HMMM...THIS WILL BE A GOOD CHANCE TO TEST MY POWER AGAIN!

$100 TO THE MAN WHO CAN STAY IN THE RING THREE MINUTES WITH **CRUSHER HOGAN**

FILLED WITH EXCITEMENT, PETE RACES BACK HOME, AND...

I'LL PUT ON SOME OLD CLOTHES, AND LEAVE MY GLASSES HERE! BUT--WHAT IF I FAIL? I DON'T WANT TO BE A LAUGHING STOCK! I–I'LL FIND SOME WAY TO **DISGUISE** MYSELF!

4

PART 2

NOW ANYBODY WITH THE INTELLIGENCE OF A SEVEN YEAR OLD KNOWS THAT IF A MAN APPEARED ON TV WHO SEEMED TO BE MORE SPIDER THAN HUMAN, HE'D BE AN OVERNIGHT SENSATION! ESPECIALLY WHEN HIS FEATS WERE PERFORMED WITHOUT THE HELP OF TRICK PHOTOGRAPHY! WELL, YOU CAN JUST IMAGINE HOW THE PUBLIC REACTED TO **SPIDERMAN!**

I'M SEEIN' IT WITH MY OWN EYES, AND I **STILL** DON'T BELIEVE IT!

V-789

SURE THEY LOOK AMAZED, INCREDIBLE, AWE-STRICKEN! WOULDN'T **YOU???**

AFTER ALL, WHEN WAS THE LAST TIME **YOU** SAW A MAN WITH HIS OWN FANTASTIC SPIDER WEB???

OKAY, SPIDERMAN-- CUT! THAT'S ENOUGH! DON'T SHOW 'EM **TOO MUCH!** LEAVE 'EM BEGGIN' FOR MORE!

7

AS HIS FIRST TV SPECTACULAR ENDS, PETER PARKER BREATHES THE FIRST SWEET SCENT OF FAME AND SUCCESS!

I'M FROM *LIFE!* WE'LL PAY ANY PRICE FOR A PICTURE SPREAD!

SIGN WITH *ME!* I'LL PUT YOU IN THE MOVIES!

WAIT! WE WANT AN INTERVIEW!

SEE MY AGENT, BOYS! I'M BUSY!

WHEW! RID OF 'EM AT LAST!

HEY! WHAT'S GOIN' ON??

STOP! THIEF! STOP HIM! IF HE MAKES IT TO THE ELEVATOR, HE'LL GET AWAY!

MADE IT!

I'M SAFE NOW! THAT COP CAN NEVER GET DOWN TO THE LOBBY AS FAST AS I CAN IN THIS HIGH-SPEED EX-PRESS ELEVATOR! LUCKY THAT GOON IN A COSTUME DIDN'T STOP ME!

WHAT'S *WITH* YOU, MISTER?? ALL YOU HADDA DO WAS TRIP HIM, OR HOLD HIM JUST FOR A MINUTE!

SORRY, PAL! THAT'S *YOUR* JOB! I'M *THRU* BEING PUSHED AROUND --BY ANYONE! FROM NOW ON I JUST LOOK OUT FOR NUMBER ONE --THAT MEANS--*ME!*

I OUGHTTA RUN YOU IN--

SAVE YOUR BREATH, BUDDY! I'VE GOT THINGS TO DO!

AND, A FEW HOURS LATER...

PETER, YOU KNOW THAT MICROSCOPE YOU'VE ALWAYS WANTED? YOUR UNCLE AND I *BOUGHT* IT FOR YOU THIS AFTERNOON!

GOSH, THAT'S TERRIFIC!

YOU'RE THE GREATEST FAMILY ANY FELLA EVER HAD!

THEY'RE THE ONLY ONES WHO'VE EVER BEEN KIND TO ME! I'LL SEE TO IT THAT *THEY'RE* ALWAYS HAPPY, BUT THE REST OF THE WORLD CAN GO HANG FOR ALL I CARE!

8

IN THE DAYS THAT FOLLOW, THE **SPIDERMAN** BECOMES THE SENSATION OF THE NATION!

SPIDERMAN SLATED FOR NEW TV SERIES!

Daily Chronicle

SPIDERMAN WINS SHOWBIZ AWARD!

The VIEWER

SPIDERMAN PLAYS TO PACKED HOUSE!

Daily Voice

WHO IS THE SPIDERMAN?

AND, ONE EVENING AS PETER PARKER RETURNS HOME FROM A PERSONAL APPEARANCE...

A POLICE CAR! IN FRONT OF OUR HOUSE! WHAT CAN BE WRONG??

BAD NEWS, SON--YOUR UNCLE HAS BEEN SHOT-- MURDERED!

UNCLE BEN --**DEAD!** NO! NO, IT **CAN'T** BE!

WHO DID IT?? **WHO SHOT HIM??**

IT WAS A BURGLAR-- YOUR UNCLE SURPRISED HIM! BUT DON'T WORRY, LAD! WE'VE GOT HIM TRAPPED! HE'S IN THE OLD ACME WAREHOUSE AT THE WATERFRONT! WE'LL GET HIM!

YOUR AUNT IS NEXT DOOR-- THE NEIGHBORS ARE LOOKING AFTER HER! WAIT--

I'VE GOT TO GO! I'VE GOT TO **GET** HIM!

I KNOW THE OLD ACME WAREHOUSE! IT'S BEEN DE- SERTED FOR YEARS! A KILLER COULD HOLD OFF AN ARMY IN THAT GLOOMY, OLD PLACE!

BUT HE WON'T HOLD OFF-- **SPIDERMAN!**

9

10

BE SURE TO SEE THE NEXT ISSUE OF *AMAZING FANTASY* --- FOR THE FURTHER AMAZING EXPLOITS OF AMERICA'S MOST *DIFFERENT* NEW TEEN-AGE IDOL -- *SPIDERMAN!*

the End

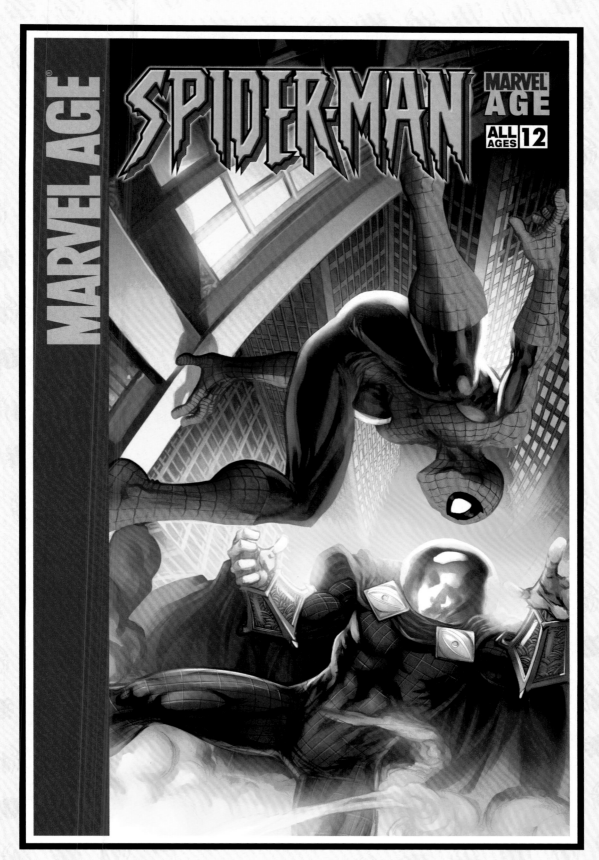

NEWCOMER **MYSTERIO** IS OUT TO RUIN SPIDER-MAN'S GOOD NAME AND SHOW WHO IS THE BETTER HERO!

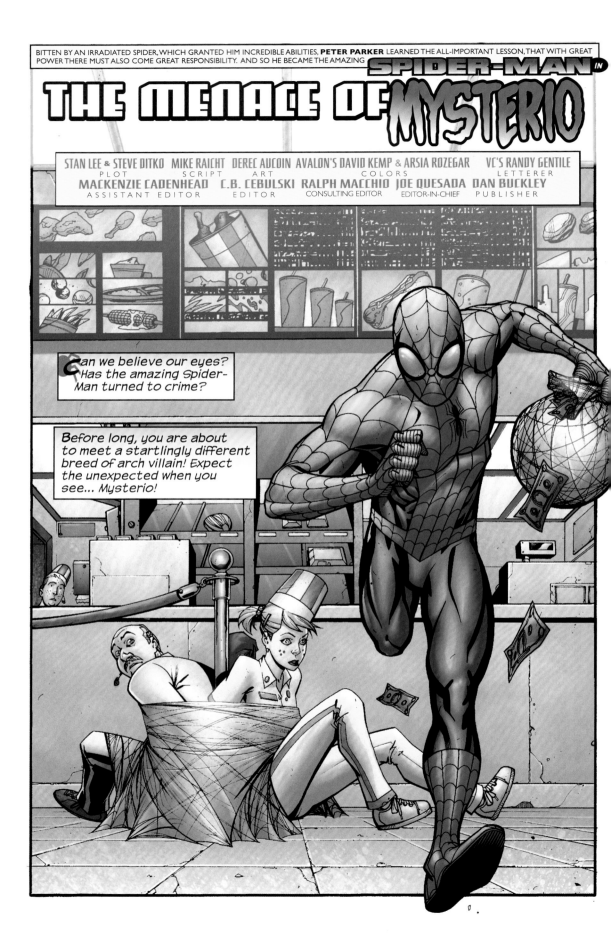

New York City...

There's no way the Knicks should have traded--

HELP!

Spider-Man ripped us off!

What th--?

Call it in quick!

It's Spider-Man!

Hey! Stop!

This is McGregor and Lewis on 40th and Park--

Whoa!

--reporting a suspected robbery in progress!

We have an officer down and Spider-Man is swinging down Park Ave and--

I'm not down. I'm fine.

--he's on 43rd now. Does anyone see him?

Forget it. He's gone.

There's no way we're catching him... and don't tell anyone I fell like that, okay?

That night, after a long and agonizing day for Peter Parker...

I'm sorry, Aunt May. I've been out of it all day.

Are you feeling okay? Do you need me to make a doctor's appointment for you? You know, to talk to someone?

I'm fine, Aunt May. I'm just tired.

Peter... if you're worried about the money it will cost, I'm not going to lie.

We're a little short, but your health is most important.

We'll get by. We always do. I want you to feel better.

Are you depressed?

No! No... like I said, I just need some sleep.

Okay, dear. Sleep tight.

Come on, Peter. Let's get some sleep.

Everything will look better in the morning.

...and this time he hit an all-night coffeehouse. At this rate Spider-Man isn't only going to be wanted-- he's going to be fat!

Ohhhhh! Burn!

Come on... what's wrong with me? Could I really be doing this in my sleep?

Later that morning. The Daily Bugle.

Hey, Peter. Are you okay? You look pretty beat.

I'm fine.

Were you out late on a big date?

Did that Liz girl finally come around?

No... I was... I just can't talk right now?

Are you sure you don't need to talk?

Seriously, Betty. I appreciate your concern but you don't understand...

I can't help if you won't talk to me about it.

I told them he was a menace, Parker, and he is! You've got pictures I assume...

Hey, Mr. Jameson. No. Not today. But I was hoping you could float me a loan.

My Aunt May and I are a little--

The best way to get money is to earn it, son.

You're a go-getter, Parker. Go get me some pictures of Spider-Man stealing something.

And then you'll get paid.

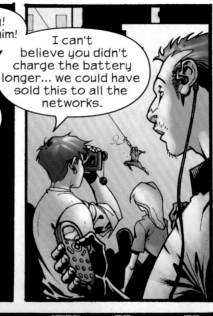

Monday morning on the way to school...

Hey, Peter, wait up.

Oh... hey, Liz.

Do you like my new hairdo?

It looks great. You look like a movie star.

Are you alright? Rough weekend? You don't look so great.

Is there anything you want to talk about? I'm here for you if you need me.

Yeah, you and everyone else.

No. I'm doing great. Really.

I'm telling you, he's innocent. There's no way Spider-Man-- whoa.

Hey, Liz! What'd you do to your hair?

Thanks a lot, Flash. See you, Peter. Let me know if you need anything.

No. I mean-- it looks-- forget it.

In JJJ's office...

I don't know. Some nutso sent me an e-mail and said he had some news about Spider-Man and he wanted to give the *Bugle* the scoop.

What's going--?

I am Mysterio!

Great. They're coming out of the woodwork. Do you guys all shop at the same store or what?

Why did you want to come to the *Bugle*?

Because you have always been anti-Spider-Man and I knew you'd take me up on my offer.

I want to bring this thief Spider-Man to justice. The only way to fight power is with power.

If you print in your paper that Spider-Man must meet me on the Brooklyn Bridge to find out the truth about himself, then I will give your paper the exclusive interview--

--with the man who brought in Spider-Man!

You've got to be kidding?!

It's genius! We'll be the hottest newspaper in the country. All the news services will pick up the story!

I don't know if it's--

Just print it! I'll write up the story myself.

So, this guy challenged Spidey to a duel?

The Next Afternoon...

Yeah, and he calls himself Mysterio! These costume guys ought to be locked up.

Did you read the description of what he was wearing?

Soon these crazies will be taking over the city.

I just don't get why they wouldn't wear something that made sense to fight in... like leather outfits or something?

The Brooklyn Bridge...? If this Mysterio guy has answers--

--I'll be there.

DAILY BUGLE
SPIDER-MAN CHALLENGED!

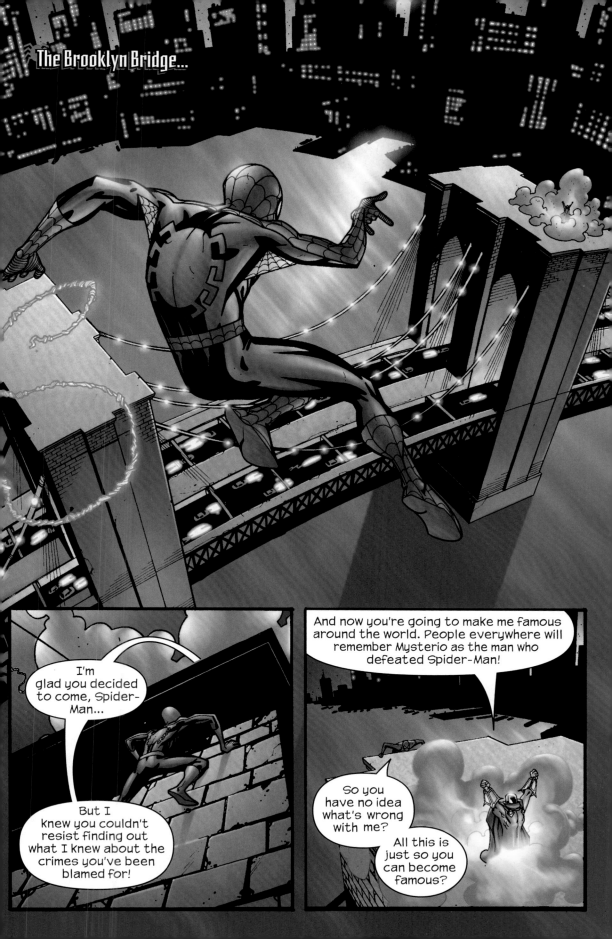

The Brooklyn Bridge...

I'm glad you decided to come, Spider-Man...

But I knew you couldn't resist finding out what I knew about the crimes you've been blamed for!

And now you're going to make me famous around the world. People everywhere will remember Mysterio as the man who defeated Spider-Man!

So you have no idea what's wrong with me?

All this is just so you can become famous?

Goodbye, Spider-Man!

Wha--?

Perfect. My public awaits!

It appears as if Spider-Man has jumped into the water to escape the mysterious vigilante known as Mysterio.

Ow...

Ow...

Oh, Peter. I was just about to wake you up. You're running late.

I didn't even hear you come in last night.

Sorry, Aunt May. I was studying with some friends at the library.

We've got a tough calculus test today.

I'm sure you'll do fine.

Aunt May, can you turn that up?

Oh my, you probably didn't know with all your studying.

That Mysterio man took care of that criminal Spider-Man.

Good riddance, I say. The *Bugle* has an exclusive with him. Your obnoxious boss announced it right after the fight.

So, if you want to hear the real scoop about what happened between Spider-Man and Mysterio on that bridge you should pick up the *Daily Bugle* tomorrow morning.

This man is a hero.

BRING BRING

Hello?

Parker. Get down to the *Bugle.* I want you to take pictures today.

Oh, um I've got school--

Well, I thought I'd give you first crack since you needed some money.

I'll be right there.

Peter, you aren't going to miss school are you?

No, I'll go down there right now. I only have gym in the morning.

Not a class or anything. Can you write me a note?

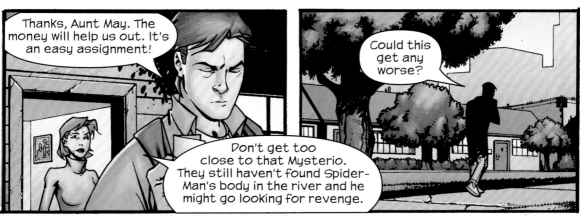

Thanks, Aunt May. The money will help us out. It's an easy assignment!

Don't get too close to that Mysterio. They still haven't found Spider-Man's body in the river and he might go looking for revenge.

Could this get any worse?

Where've you been, Parker?

I came as fast as I could.

The Daily Bugle.

Mysterio has promised to reveal Spider-Man's identity the next time they fight...

...if the creep is still alive.

Really? How's he going to do that?

All will be revealed shortly.

How does he do that? That's great!

What does he mean, all will be revealed?

It's going to be in the paper tomorrow, but he's also going to announce his intentions on Channel 2 tonight.

We both agreed you could never get too much coverage! He's a celebrity now. The flavor of the week!

And he'll be a guest on David Lett--

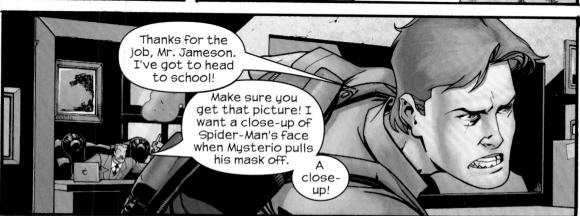

Thanks for the job, Mr. Jameson. I've got to head to school!

Make sure you get that picture! I want a close-up of Spider-Man's face when Mysterio pulls his mask off. A close-up!

Later that night...

Oh, you've got to be kidding me. He's giving autographs?!?

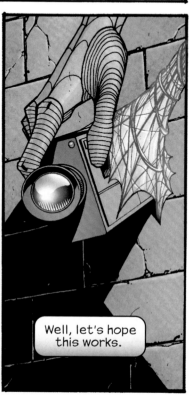

Well, let's hope this works.

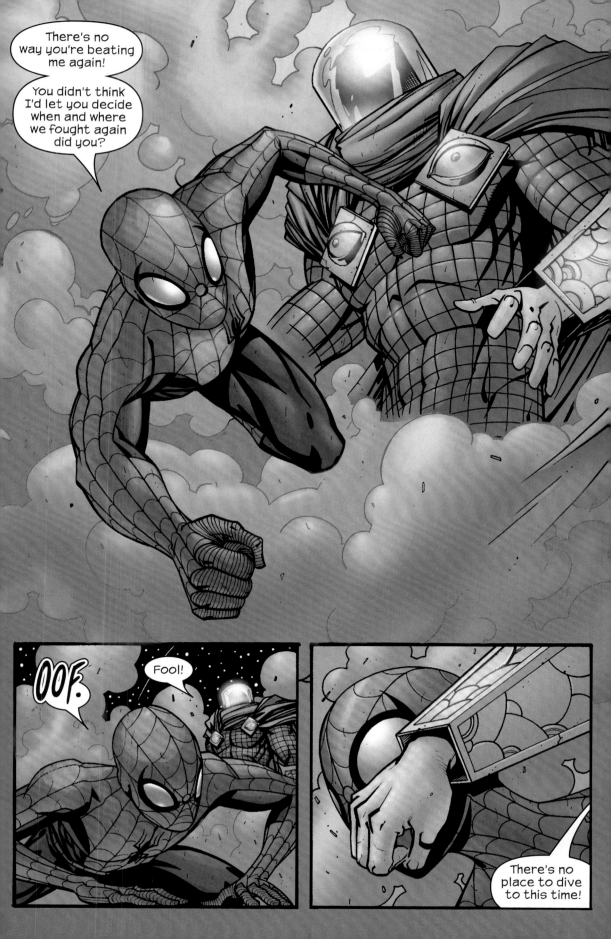

I've worked too hard to have you defeat me now!

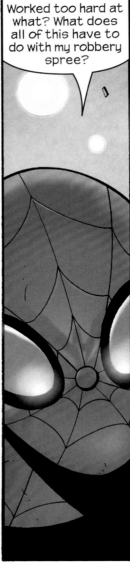

Worked too hard at what? What does all of this have to do with my robbery spree?

You actually believed you were behind those robberies?

What did you think, you were Dr. Jekyll and Mr. Hyde when you went to bed?

I was a special-effects maker in Hollywood...

...I watched you on TV and wondered if I could do those things. Create props to help me perform those amazing stunts.

And I could.

So, you robbed all those places as me? But why become Mysterio?

Because after I used you to make the money I decided I wanted to be the hero, too.

SURPRISE! I was just faking ya!

Man, I didn't know how much longer I could listen to that!

I can't believe you actually confessed!

Wait!

No waiting! I just hope the police accept your confession.

I just hope I don't get in trouble for borrowing this from school.

Oh man, now I'm talking, giving away my life story, just like Mysterio. He's not even conscious.

Now say cheese, Mysterio.

The next morning in homeroom...

DAILY BUGLE
EXTRA EDITION

DUPED! MYSTERIO DANGEROUS CON MAN
J. JONAH JAMESON EXCLUSIVE REPORT. HOW HE HELPED CAPTURE MYSTERIO.

The paper said that Mysterio confessed to everything on the tape.

I told you guys!

DAILY BUGLE
DUPED! MYSTERIO DANGEROUS CON MAN

It doesn't prove anything. They should lock them both up.

They were probably in on it together.

You and your conspiracies.

What do you think, Peter?

RING RING

Who cares what he thinks, Liz.

Flash, be nice. He's one of the smartest guys in school.

Smarter than you anyway.

I don't care how smart he is...

...he doesn't know a thing about Spider-Man.

End.

IN THIS MODERN ADAPTATION OF SPIDER-MAN'S AMAZING ORIGIN,
PETER PARKER TRULY LEARNS THAT WITH GREAT POWER, THERE MUST ALSO COME GREAT RESPONSIBILITY.

Sure, you've heard of Spider-Man. You know all about his amazing powers.

But who is he, really? Where did he come from? And when did he start weaving his tangled webs?

Looks like *Peter Parker* doesn't have anyone to sit with.

There's an empty seat next to me.

Are you *kiddin'*? That *dweeb* comes within spittin' distance and my *reputation* starts to slide. Let him eat *alone!*

Yeah, he's probably got some important *reading* to do, anyway. Like, "The Total Loser's Guide to *Everything.*"

Ha! *Good one,* man!

BITTEN BY AN IRRADIATED SPIDER, WHICH GRANTED HIM INCREDIBLE ABILITIES, **PETER PARKER** LEARNED THE ALL-IMPORTANT LESSON, THAT WITH GREAT POWER THERE MUST ALSO COME GREAT RESPONSIBILITY.

ERE COMES SPIDER-MAN

KITTY FROSS
WRITER

PATRICK SCHERBERGER
PENCILS

NORMAN LEE
INKS

GURU eFX'S HARTMAN and BEVARD
COLORS

DAVE SHARPE
LETTERER

JAMES TAVERAS
PRODUCTION

JOHN BARBER
ASST. EDITOR

MACKENZIE CADENHEAD
EDITOR

MARK PANICCIA
CONSULTING EDITOR

JOE QUESADA
CHIEF

DAN BUCKLEY
PUBLISHER

Adapted from AMAZING FANTASY #15 by STAN LEE and STEVE DITKO

Queens, NY

It's true...Peter Parker was nobody's idea of a super hero. But that didn't stop his Uncle Ben and Aunt May from thinking he was just....

Super, Peter! Another *A+* in *Calculus*! Those scouts from *Harvard*'ll be beating your door down soon!

Oh, Uncle Ben...it's no big deal!

We're both so *proud* of you, dear.

Thanks, Aunt May. I gotta run to school. See you tonight!

Now, Peter. You need to *bundle up*. It's *chilly* out there today!

Don't *worry*. I'll be *fine*!

That evening...

EXPERIMENTS IN RADIOACTIVITY 3RD FLOOR

So *what* if no one wanted to come to this exhibit with me...no one at Midtown High could understand the far-reaching *implications* of this work anyway!

Of course, the *technology* has *improved* so much that we can now pinpoint the tiniest target with a *radioactive beam...*

Which is vital, given that anything that's exposed to this amount of *radiation* will be *mutated* in ways that we are still unable to predict...

The Parker Residence

You're home early...how was the exhibit?

Peter! You look *terrible*! What on earth is the *matter*?

Have to get up to *bed*... can't collapse in front of Aunt May and Uncle Ben. It'll *scare* them to *death*!

I'm OK... I think I'm just coming down with the flu or some- thing.

He's just burning up!

Let's let the boy rest. We'll call the doctor in the morning if he's not feeling better...

The next day...

Good morning, dear. How are you feeling today?

Great, Aunt May. I guess whatever I had was a 12-hour thing!

Sorry, I've gotta make tracks. I'll grab breakfast at school.

Goodness, Peter, you're *crushing* the breath right out of me! You really *must* be feeling better!

Good thing I have study hall first period. I didn't even do any of my homework last night...

Watch where you're *going,* ya *dumb kid!*

Whoa!

Okay... this is *not* normal!

Mommy, *look!* There's a *man* crawling up that *building!*

That's it! No more *comic books* for you, young man.

Definitely not normal!

Tomorrow night? Yeah, I'm available. Sure, yeah, I can put on a show.

Don't you worry about a thing!

Time to get to *work*...

This polymer should be just as *strong* and *flexible*, pound for pound, as a *spider's web*...I guess all that hard work in *Chemistry Lab* is finally paying off!

Hey, Sport, you've been at it all afternoon. Why don't you take a little *break*? How 'bout a game of cards?

I can't right now, Uncle Ben. I'm really *busy*.

Aw, sure, I understand. Maybe *later*...

Sure, Uncle Ben, later.

Yeah, later...unless I'm too busy teaching those football-playing *muscle-heads* how it feels to be the weakling... or maybe picking up Liz in my *new Beamer*...

Dude! That was *awesome!*

Do you do birthdays? Bar mitzvahs?

I represent a *sporting goods* company. I'd like to talk to you about a line of *Spider-Man sneakers...*

Spidey, can I have your *autograph?*

See my agent, folks. I've got places to be.

Stop! Thief! Hey, you, in the costume, *stop him!* He's getting away!

Thanks, pal. I owe ya one!

‹pant› Why didn't you *stop* him?! Now I'll never catch him!

Sorry, buddy, but that's *your* problem.

From now on, I'm looking out for *Number One!*

I wonder if anyone at Midtown caught my act tonight...

I bet Flash'd be totally--

A *police car*...in front of our house!

Aunt May... Uncle Ben...

Let me *through!* I live here!

Son, *wait!* There's something you need to *know*...

Let 'im go. It's better if he hears it from *her* anyway.

Aunt May! What is it? *What's happened?*

Oh, Peter...

Peter, it's your Uncle Ben. He's...he's *dead!*

Peter, *wait!*

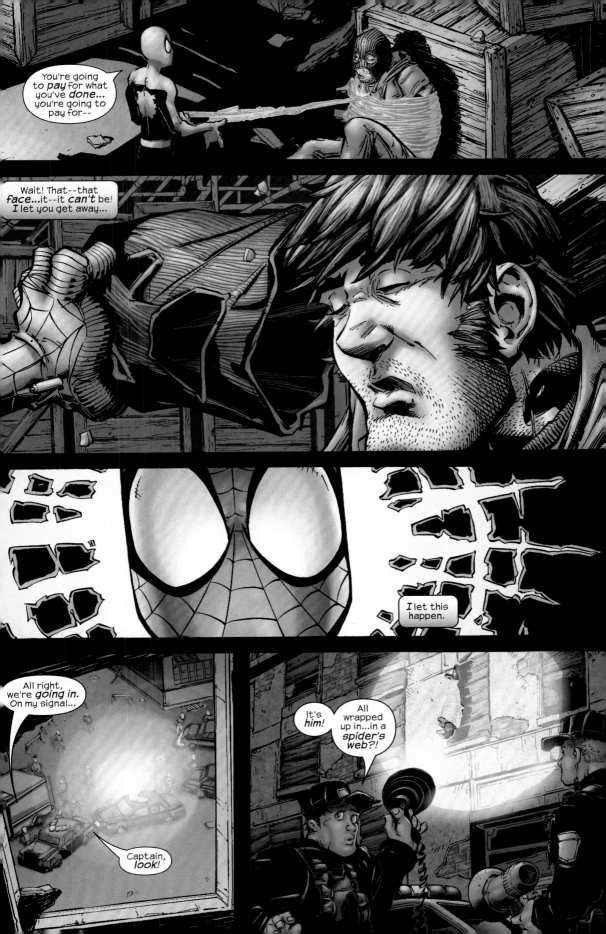

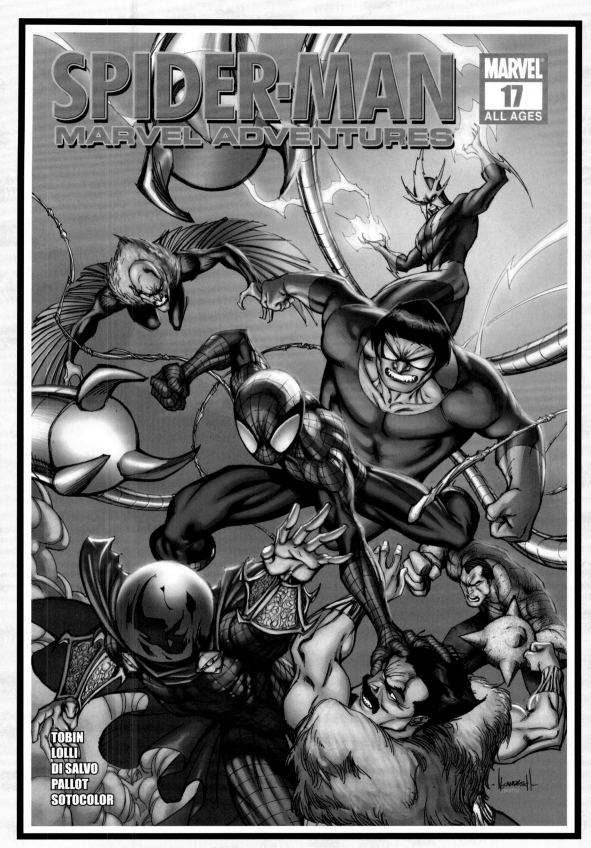

THE **SINISTER SIX** HAS RETURNED AND IS AFTER SPIDER-MAN, THOUGH THEY SEEM TO BE DOWN A MEMBER.

SPIDER-MAN! YOU'RE MY HERO!

NOT A PROBLEM.

EVERY HERO HAS TO DO HIS PART. SOMETIMES, SAVING THE DAY MEANS A CHAOTIC *BATTLE* AGAINST THE *RED GHOST* AND HIS *SUPER APES!*

OTHER TIMES, SAVING THE DAY MEANS...

...HOLDING UP A CAR SO THAT YOU CAN CHANGE A FLAT.

GETTING A LITTLE *HEAVY*, THOUGH! I WOULDN'T MIND IF A FEW *OTHER* NEW YORKERS WERE WILLING TO LEND A...

LOOK OUT, SPIDEY!

...TENTACLE?

SPIDER-MAN!

AWWW, NO! MY CAR!

AWWW, NO! DOCTOR OCTOPUS AND HIS SINISTER SIX!

SIX-TO-ONE-SHOT!

WRITER - PAUL TOBIN   **PENCILS** - MATTEO LOLLI   **INKER** - TERRY PALLOT
COLORS - SOTOCOLOR   **LETTERS** - DAVE SHARPE   **COVER** - GARZA & SOTO
ASST. EDITOR · RACHEL PINNELAS   **ASSOC. EDITOR** - TOM BRENNAN   **SENIOR EDITOR** - STEPHEN WACKER
EDITOR IN CHIEF · AXEL ALONSO   **CHIEF CREATIVE OFFICER** ·JOE QUESADA   **PUBLISHER** · DAN BUCKLEY   **EXECUTIVE PRODUCER** · ALAN FINE

BUT...WHY ARE YOU ALL IN FORMAL WEAR?

ARE YOU CATERING A WEDDING?

HEY! WILL YOU HAVE THOSE DELICIOUS LITTLE HOT DOGS?

YOU KNOW WHY WE'RE IN THESE SUITS. AFTER ALL, YOU'RE THE ONE WHO DESTROYED OUR PLANS!

WEEKS OF PLANNING, NOW... USELESS! THANKS TO YOU!

SERIOUSLY... YOU GUYS CAN THANK ME LATER!

ALSO, I HAVE NO IDEA WHAT YOU'RE TALKING ABOUT! I FOILED YOUR PLANS? HOW?

SERIOUSLY, THOUGH. EXACTLY *WHAT IS IT* THAT I'M SUPPOSED TO HAVE *DONE?*

YOU CAN *DROP* THE *PRETENSE.* THE VULTURE *CALLED ME* FROM JAIL! HE TOLD ME *EVERY-THING!*

"HE TOLD ME HOW HE HAD BEEN DRESSED IN HIS SUIT, READY TO MEET UP WITH US AS SCHEDULED."

CAN'T *BELIEVE* I FORGOT MY SUIT. BUT...NO PROBLEM. I'LL JUST *STEAL* ONE FROM THIS STORE.

"AND HE TOLD US HOW *YOU* ARRIVED FROM NOWHERE, PUNCHING HIM FROM BEHIND!"

MIGHT AS WELL TAKE THIS *PURSE,* LONG AS I'M AT IT! A FEW EXTRA DOLLARS *ALWAYS* COME IN HANDY!

AUNT MAY! JUST LET HIM *HAVE* IT!

"HE TOLD US OF THE *FIERCE* BATTLE. HOW HE'D BEEN ON THE VERGE OF *VICTORY* BEFORE GETTING SNARED BY YOUR *CURSED WEBBING!*"

YOU! I'VE LIVED IN NEW YORK *ALL* MY LIFE! IT'S THE *GREATEST* CITY IN THE *WORLD!* IT HAS MORE *CULTURE* AND MORE *GOOD PEOPLE* THAN SOME ENTIRE COUNTRIES!

BUT IT'S PEOPLE LIKE *YOU* THAT GIVE IT A MENACING REPUTATION!

AUNT MAY...HE'S NOT LISTENING!

"AND NOW HE'S IN JAIL. BUT HE'LL *ESCAPE*...THE FOOLS HAVEN'T TAKEN HIS *WINGS!*"

NICE COSTUME, ELECTRO!

I REMEMBER ONCE WHEN I WAS IN A *GRADE SCHOOL PLAY* AND I ALSO PLAYED A *FLOWER!*

I AM NOT DRESSED AS A *FLOWER!*

BUT I WAS LIKE...*WAY* TOO ENTHUSIASTIC! RUINED EVERYTHING. I WAS THE *WORST* DANDELION IN THE WHOLE PLAY.

BY THE WAY...WHAT TYPE OF FLOWER ARE *YOU* SUPPOSED TO BE? A *DAISY?*

I AM *NOT* A *FLOWER!* THIS MASK REPRESENTS *ELECTRICAL BOLTS!*

HERE'S MORE *FLOWERS* FOR YOU, *DAISY!*

THAT'S *IT!*

ELECTRO! CALM *DOWN!*

Meanwhile: 122 blocks away.

IT'S JUST A *PURSE.* I'VE STOLEN *PURSES* BEFORE. WHY DO I FEEL SO BAD ABOUT *THIS* ONE?

I NEED TO CALM DOWN.

THAT *SO?* WELL, THERE'S ONLY *ONE THING* TO *DO* THEN!

BEEP! BEEP! *BEEP-BEEP!*

HE'S *TOO FAST!*

JUST KEEP THE *PRESSURE* ON HIM! AND *DON'T* LET HIM DRAW US INTO ATTACKING *EACH OTHER,* LIKE HE DID BEFORE!

BEEP! BEEP! *BEEP-BEEP!*

FIGHT *BACK-TO-BACK!* THAT WAY WE'LL MAKE SURE *NOT* TO HIT *EACH OTHER!*

BEEP! BEEP! *BEEP-BEEP!*

AND... *WHY* ARE YOU MAKING THAT INFERNAL *BEEPING* NOISE? HAVE YOU GONE *INSANE?*

OH, SORRY!

IT'S JUST THAT'S THE NOISE YOU'RE *SUPPOSED* TO MAKE...

...WHEN YOU'RE BACKING UP A TRUCK!

WHUMMPFF

UNHHHH.

OHHHHH.

NO. NO. PAY *ATTENTION!* IT'S NOT "UNHHHH" OR "OHHHH." IT'S "BEEP! BEEP! BEEP-BEEP!"

AHHH. *NEVER MIND.* YOU GUYS JUST *NEVER* LEARN, DO YOU?

I MEAN, SERIOUSLY, YOU DIDN'T EVEN SAY *"THANKS"* FOR ME ONLY USING ABOUT HALF MY STRENGTH WITH THE TRUCK!

THERE'S PROBABLY A COURSE ON *SOCIAL MANNERS* OFFERED IN PRISON. YOU GUYS SHOULD *DEFINITELY* SIGN UP!

Two hours later.
Queens.
Home of Peter and Aunt May Parker.

...AND HE JUST *TOOK MY PURSE!* JUST TOOK IT AND *FLEW AWAY!* THIS CITY IS FULL OF THIEVES!

SOMEONE'S AT THE *DOOR,* AUNT MAY.

COULD *YOU* GET THAT, PETER? I'M ALL IN A *MOOD.*

SURE, SURE. IT'S PROBABLY JUST SOME *ADVERTISER,* OR A...

KNOCK KNOCK KNOCK

...deliveryman.

HERE.

I FOUND THIS ADDRESS INSIDE THE PURSE.

COULD YOU...COULD YOU DO ME A *FAVOR?* JUST TELL THE WOMAN WHO OWNS THIS PURSE THAT... NEW YORK *IS* THE GREATEST CITY ON EARTH.

HUH. MAYBE... MAYBE YOU GUYS DO LEARN SOMETHING, NOW AND THEN.

WHAT A *WEIRD* DAY. WHAT A WEIRD *TOWN.* I LOVE IT.

CLICK

The end.

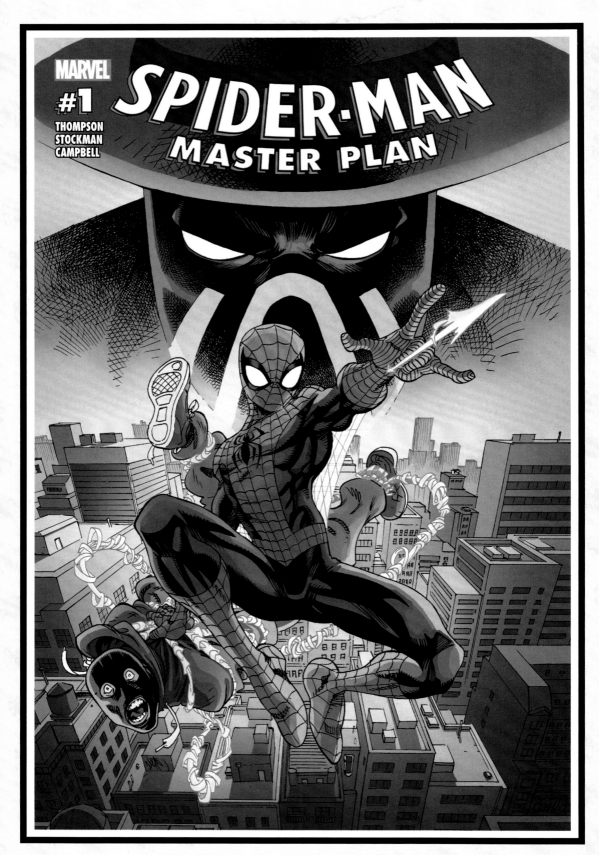

ALL **PETER PARKER** WANTS TO DO IS ENJOY A QUIET NIGHT AT THE THEATER,
WHICH IS DIFFICULT WHEN THE CITY IS EXPERIENCING A CRIME WAVE!

MY NAME IS PETER PARKER.

AND I'M TOTALLY AND COMPLETELY LATE.

IT'S POSSIBLE I'M ALSO TOTALLY AND COMPLETELY DISORGANIZED.

BUT I CAN DO THIS. I CAN!

CAN I DO THIS?

OKAY, AUNT MAY'S DRY CLEANING DROPPED OFF. PACKAGES MAILED. HOMEWORK MOSTLY DONE. YES. I CAN DO THIS. I CAN! BECAUSE THERE'S NO WAY I'M MISSING...

...THIS.

I'VE BEEN WAITING MONTHS TO SEE THIS SHOW. AND THERE'S NO WAY I'M GONNA MISS--

SPIDEY-SENSES ON HIGH ALERT, WHICH MEANS...

HEY, THAT'S MY CAR!

N.B.D.

I CAN DO THIS.

CAN I DO THIS?

OKAY, MAYBE *I* CAN'T DO THIS.

BUT SPIDER-MAN SURE CAN!

THWIP

MASTER PLAN

ROBBIE THOMPSON
writer

NATHAN STOCKMAN
artist

JIM CAMPBELL
colorist

VC's TRAVIS LANHAM letterer   MARK BASSO editor
AXEL ALONSO editor in chief   JOE QUESADA chief creative officer
DAN BUCKLEY president   ALAN FINE executive producer

SPIDER-MAN created by STAN LEE & STEVE DITKO

GET THAT LITTLE FREAK!

HEY, WHO YOU CALLIN' *LITTLE*?

WHAK

OOOF!

THANKS, SKI-MASKED HOOLIGAN NUMBER 2. I AGREE. NAME-CALLING IS SO NOT COOL.

OH, DON'T WORRY, FELLAS, I DIDN'T FORGET ABOUT YOU TWO.

Y'KNOW, YOU'RE THE *SECOND* GUY TO CALL ME THAT TONIGHT.

AS I WAS JUST SAYING: WHAT IS GOING ON HERE?

WAS THERE A SALE ON SKI MASKS?

IS THERE A CRIME CONVENTION IN TOWN?

WAIT. IS CRIMECON A THING?

I...I DUNNO. HE... HE JUST TOLD US ALL TO GO WILD. HAD ALL THESE LEADS ON SCORES. WAS HANDING 'EM OUT LIKE CANDY ON HALLOWEEN.

WHAT IS IT WITH CRIMINALS AND CANDY ANALOGIES?

DON'T ANSWER THAT. ANSWER THIS: HE WHO?

HE WHO WHAT?

THE GUY WHO WAS HANDING OUT THE LEADS.

NEVER GOT A NAME. JUST GOT A DATE AND TIME.

LEMME GUESS: TODAY. NOW.

YOU GOT IT, YOU FILTHY

THWIP

COORDINATED ATTACKS. BUT THE ATTACKS ARE RANDOM. WHY IS THIS HAPPENING? AND WHO IS BEHIND IT?

OKAY. THIS VIEW ISN'T REALLY NARROWING IT DOWN FOR ME. SO, LET'S GET A CLOSER LOOK-SEE...

OKAY, LET'S MAP ALL THESE ATTACKS. SEE IF THERE'S A PATTERN.

QUEENS

MANHATTAN

BROOKLYN

HOLY BUCKETS, THEY'RE EVERYWHERE.

MANHATTAN

UPPER EAST SI

Central P

HELL'S KITCHEN

Times Square

MIDTOWN

State Building

WAIT... THEY'RE EVERYWHERE BUT...

STARK TOWER!

THESE ARE ALL DISTRACTIONS FOR A *BIGGER* JOB!

STARK TOWER

PERFECT. ONLY A DOZEN MORE CRIMES BETWEEN ME AND STARK TOWER...I CAN STOP ALL THESE CRIMES, OR STOP WHOEVER'S ROBBING THE TOWER.

NO. I CAN DO BOTH.

CAN I DO BOTH?

STARK

KZZZZT

I WAS LOOKING FOR A FALL GUY.

YAAGHH!

BUT A SPIDER WILL DO JUST FINE.

YOU GOTTA BE KIDD--

MAYBE I NEED A DAY PLANNER. OR I COULD START A BULLET JOURNAL. I MEAN, IF CRIME MASTER CAN BE ORGANIZED, CAN'T I?

WELL, THE DAY'S NOT A TOTAL WASH. I GOT MY ERRANDS DONE.

AND HEY, I SAVED THE DAY, THAT'S GOTTA BE--

OH, COME ON...

BREAKING NEWS
SPIDER-MAN ON CRIME SPREE WITH CRIME MASTER

7

I'M GONNA TAKE THAT AS MY CUE TO CALL IT A NIGH--!!

WHAT *ELSE* COULD POSSIBLY HAPPEN TONIGHT?

BETTER LATE THAN NEVER.

HERE YA GO, SLUGGER!

UM, ACTUALLY, IT'S SPIDER-MAN.

THANKS, BUG MAN.

EW. SPIDERS ARE GROSS.

I JUST *HAD* TO WISH FOR THAT CAT IN A TREE.

THE END.

THE **WEB-WARRIORS** ARE ON THE SCENE TO PROTECT THE MULTIVERSE,
BUT WHAT WILL HAPPEN WHEN THEY RUN INTO DOCTOR OCTOPUS?

Earth-177.

ONE OF COUNTLESS EARTHS ALL CONNECTED TO A MULTIVERSAL *WEB OF LIFE* AND *DESTINY.*

NOW, A PINPRICK OF LIGHT APPEARS IN THE SKIES ABOVE THIS WORLD'S GREATEST METROPOLIS-- NEW YORK CITY...TWELFTH AVENUE TO BE EXACT.

THROUGH THE ENLARGING APERTURE, A QUINTET OF HEROES WILL APPEAR SUCH AS THIS REALITY HAS NEVER SEEN...

...DIVERSE IN BACKGROUND, YET UNITED IN A SPIRIT OF ADVENTURE AND DESIRE FOR JUSTICE.

THEY ARE KNOWN FAR AND WIDE AS--

WEB-WARRIORS-- WE MADE IT!

WHAT-- NO WELCOMING COMMITTEE? WE MAKE A GRAND ENTRANCE AND NOBODY'S AROUND TO SEE IT? NUTS!

I HEAR YA, *GHOST-SPIDER!* IT'S LIKE MY BAND THE *SPIDER-SLAYERS* GIVING A CONCERT IN AN EMPTY CLUB.

COME ON, *SPIDER-PUNK.* IT'S NOT MY FAULT THE WRIST TELEPORTERS TOOK US TO A SPARSELY POPULATED PART OF THE CITY.

SHOULDN'T WE HAVE A BATTLE CRY LIKE THE AVENGERS? HOWZABOUT *"WEB-WARRIORS WOW?!"* MAYBE *"WEB-WARRIORS WHA?"*

HELP ME OUT HERE.

IN GOG WE TRUST!

RALPH MACCHIO writer · FLAVIANO artist
ERICK ARCINIEGA colorist · VC's TRAVIS LANHAM letterer
EDUARD PETROVICH cover artist

IN A *PIG'S EYE* WE CAN'T! NO OFFENSE, SPIDER-HAM.

APPARENTLY YOU'RE NO DIFFERENT THAN ANY OTHER DOCTOR OCTOPUS. JUST A LITTLE SLICKER ON FIRST BLUSH. BOOORRRING!

BUT WE'LL STOP YOU WITH A LITTLE HELP FROM OUR *NEW* FRIEND--GOG!

HA! HIGHLY UNLIKELY. ALL MY ASSISTANTS-- INCLUDING GOG--ARE UNDER MY COMPLETE *MENTAL CONTROL!*

I BLANKETED THIS FACILITY FOR YEARS WITH A SPECIFIC *RADIATION FREQUENCY* THAT FOSTERED MY CONTROL OF ALL HERE.

I STILL HAVE NEED OF GOG--AND WHILE I DO, I'LL NEVER ALLOW HIM TO ACHIEVE FULL STATURE.

GUESS WE JUST HAVEN'T BEEN IN YOUR OCTOPUS' GARDEN LONG ENOUGH TO SAP OUR WILLS TOO.

IT'S ALMOST SECOND NATURE FOR SPIDER-MEN TO TAKE YOU DOWN ON *ANY* EARTH, OCK.

YEAH. WHAT HE SAID, GOGGLES!

GENTLEMEN, LET'S SHOW THESE INFERIOR SPIDER-MEN WHAT THEY'RE UP AGAINST.

TRANSFORM, MY--

--SINISTER SIX!

The End.

MARVEL STUDIOS

SPIDER-MAN
Far From Home

IMAGE GALLERY